My Activity Book 3

Whole Class
Independent Work
Units 19-26, Review (1-26), Vowel Review

Slanted Text Version

Critical Foundations in Primary Reading

Marilyn Sprick, Shelley V. Jones, Richard Dunn, Barbara Gunn

ISBN 13-digit: 978-1-59318-857-3
ISBN 10-digit: 1-59318-857-9

148890

Printed in the United States of America.

Published and Distributed by

17855 Dallas Parkway, Suite 400 • Dallas, TX 75287 • 800 547-6747
www.voyagerlearning.com

I'm

Review

Student's Challenge: Find and circle the four hidden Bb's.

Dear Family: Ask your child to tell you about this page. "What letter are you studying?" (b) • "What in the picture begins with b?" (bees and buckets) • "What letters are at the bottom of the page?" (y, p, c, r)

1

I'm _____

My Letter <u>B</u> Book

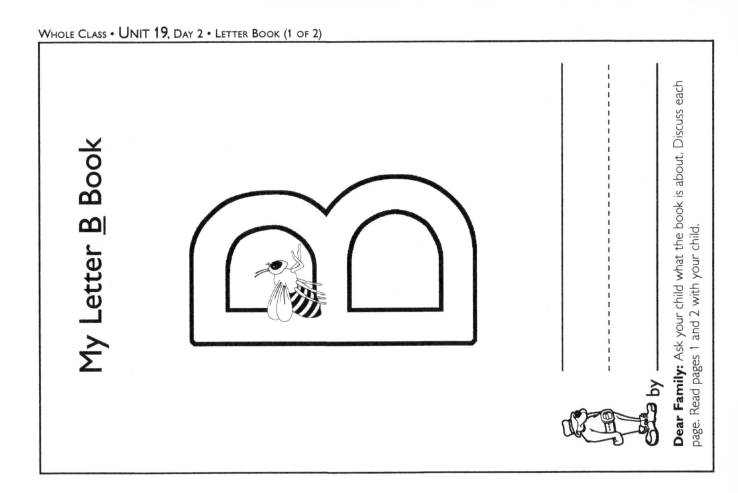

by _____

Dear Family: Ask your child what the book is about. Discuss each page. Read pages 1 and 2 with your child.

Other sounds I know about:

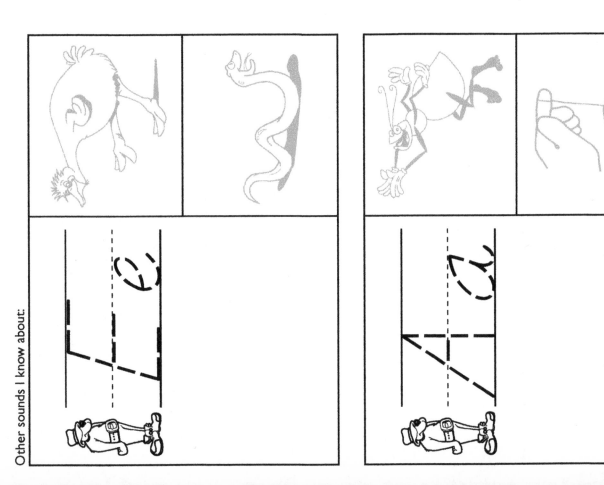

3 Have students cross out the picture that does not start with the sound.

See the

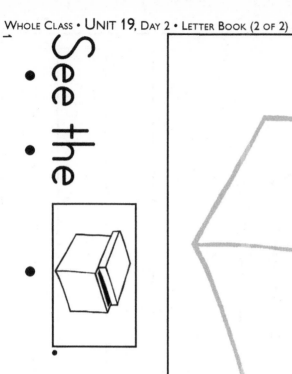

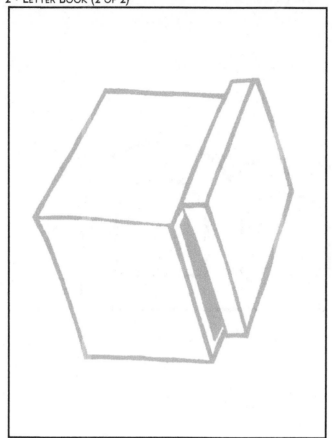

I see 1

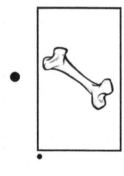

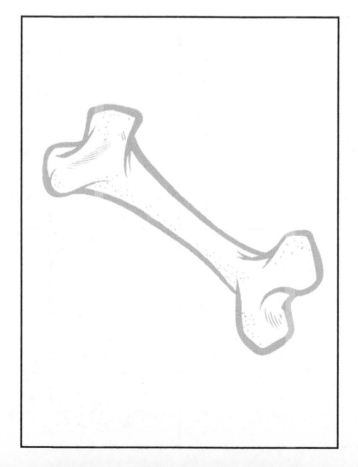

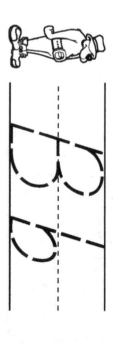

4

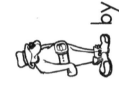

Bee Facts

by _____

Dear Family: Please read the book with your child. Questions and prompts are labeled "Adult Says."

▲ End

Adult Says: What are two ways bees use to talk to each other?

Student Says: the waggle dance and buzzing

3

● Beginning

■ Middle

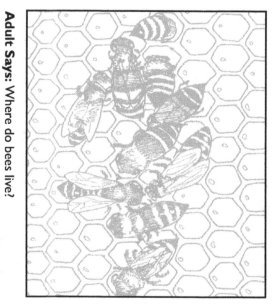

Adult Says: Where do bees live?

Student Says: in a hive

1

Adult Says: How many body parts does a bee have?

Student Says: three

Adult Says: How many legs does a bee have?

Student Says: six

2

I m

STUDENT DIRECTIONS: Color and cut out the pictures. Then sort and glue them. Glue the things that start with /nnn/ under the circle with the n. Glue the things that start with /b/ under the circle with the b.

n

b

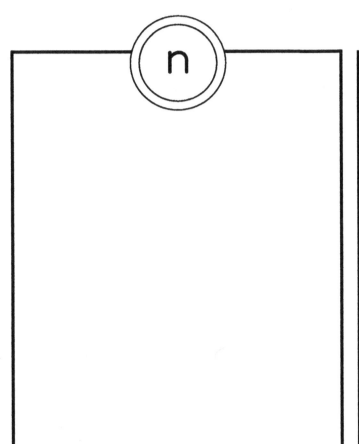

7

PREP: Copy one puzzle piece page per student on white paper. (You may wish to cut the puzzle pieces into four sections. Students can cut each section into two pieces or simply match and glue them as is to the frame.) Copy one frame per student on colored paper. Make a sample. Have extra copies of the puzzle pieces in case some get lost.

STUDENT DIRECTIONS: Color the puzzle pieces, if time allows. Cut out the puzzle pieces. Match and glue the pieces to the frame. Practice reading the words.

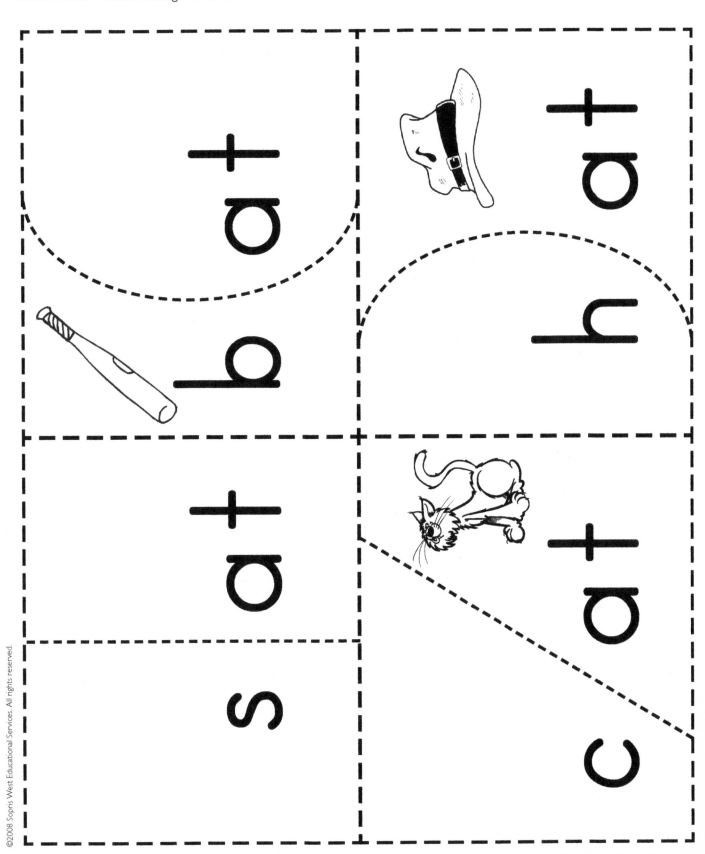

Dear Family: Read the words with your child.

I'm _____

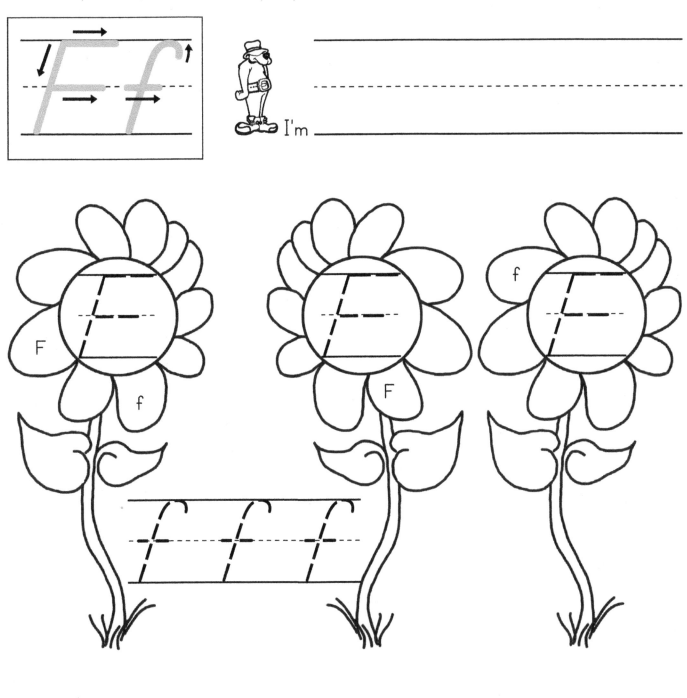

I'm _____

Review

Student's Challenge: Find and circle the four hidden _Ff_'s.
Dear Family: Ask your child to tell you about this page. "What letter are you studying?" (f) • "What in the picture begins with f?" (flowers) • "What letters are at the bottom of the page?" (b, t, d, s)

I'm _____

My Letter F Book

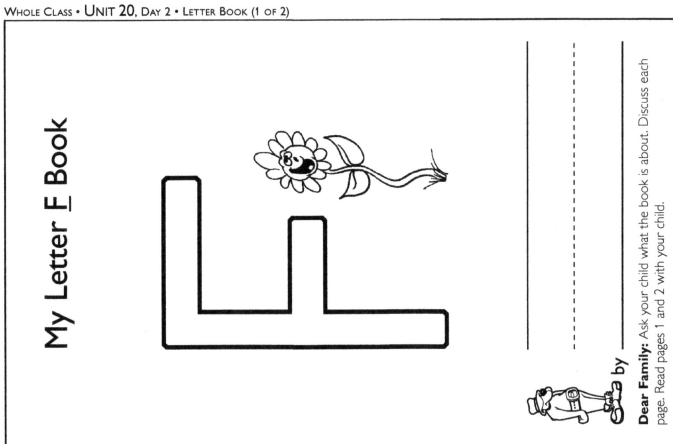

Dear Family: Ask your child what the book is about. Discuss each page. Read pages 1 and 2 with your child.

by _____

Other sounds I know about:

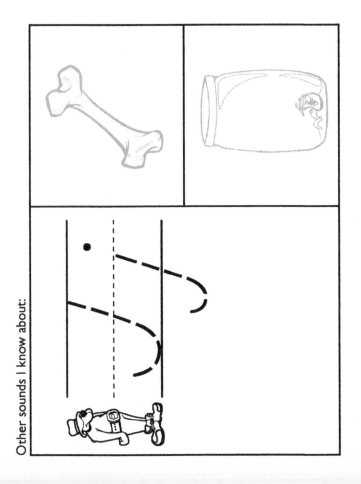

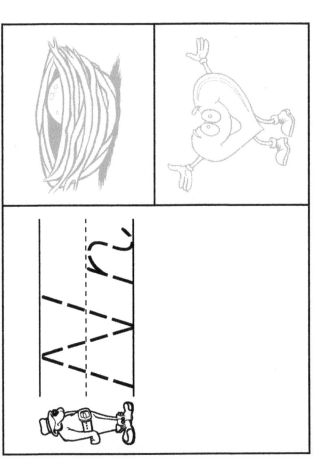

3 Have students cross out the picture that does not start with the sound.

15

I see 3

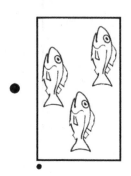

1

See the

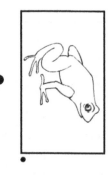

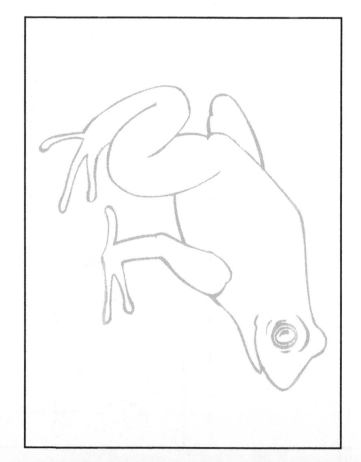

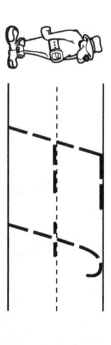

2

Felicia's Flower
Retell Book

_____

by

Dear Family: Please read the book with your child. Questions and prompts are labeled "Adult Says."

▲ End

Adult Says: At the end of the story, what did Felicia help her neighbors get?

Student Says: seeds

Adult Says: What did they use the seeds for?

Student Says: beautiful gardens

3

1

● Beginning

Adult Says: At the beginning of the story, what was Felicia's favorite thing?

Student Says: her garden

■ Middle

Adult Says: In the middle of the story, what did the big seed that Felicia planted grow into?

Student Says: a sunflower

2

See Ed

by _____

I had a

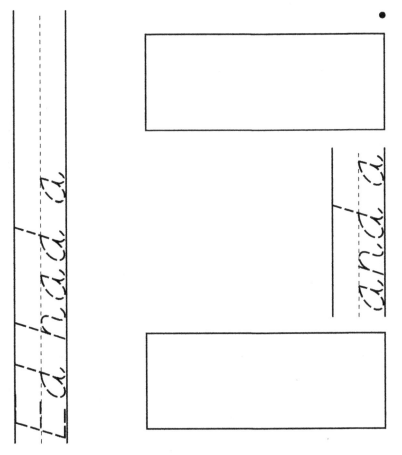

and a

4

2

El had a

3

PREP: Copy one word page per student on white paper. (You may wish to cut the sentences into strips for students who need assistance. Students can cut the strips into pieces, or simply match and glue the strips.) Copy one frame page per student on colored paper. Make a sample. Have extra copies of the puzzle pieces in case some get lost.

STUDENT DIRECTIONS: Cut out the word boxes and put them in one place so they won't get lost. Arrange the word boxes to make sentences and glue the pieces to the frame. Read the sentences to yourself or a partner.

21

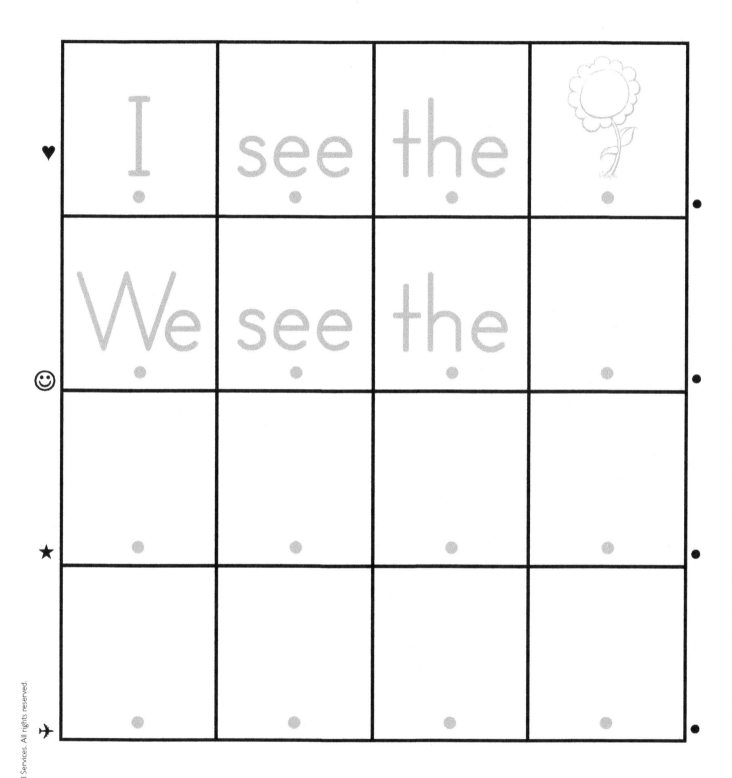

Dear Family: Point to the words and have your child read each sentence with you. Next, have your child point to the words and read the sentence. Congratulate your child on his or her ability to read the sentence.

I'm _____

Review

Student's Challenge: Find and circle the four hidden Gg's.
Dear Family: Ask your child to tell you about this page. "What letter are you studying?" (g) • "What in the picture begins with g?" (goose and grass) • "What letters are at the bottom of the page?" (f, v, i, w)

I'm _____

My Letter G Book

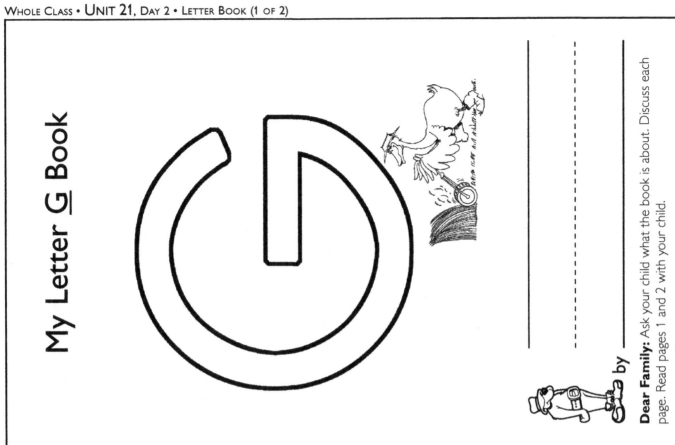

by _____

Dear Family: Ask your child what the book is about. Discuss each page. Read pages 1 and 2 with your child.

Other sounds I know about:

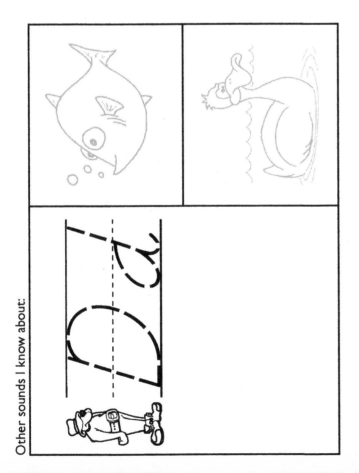

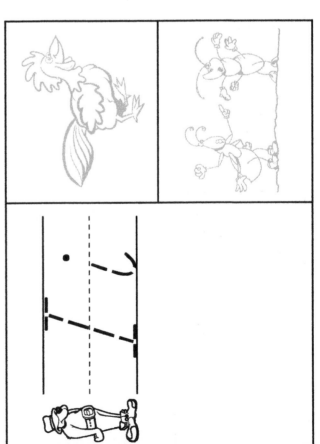

3 Have students cross out the picture that does not start with the sound.

See 2

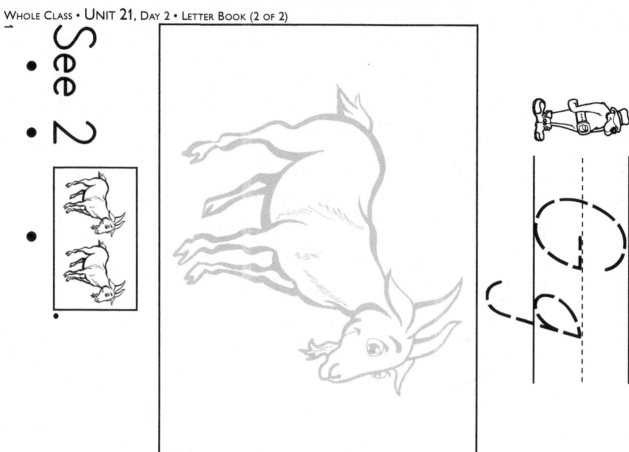

See the

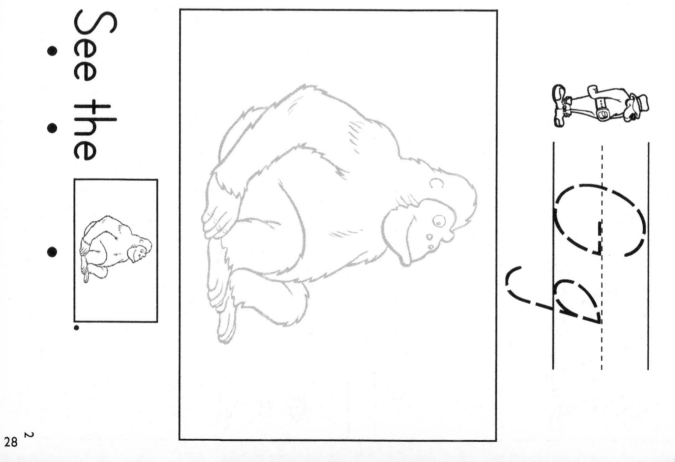

Goose, Goose, Goose, Goose, Duck

Retell Book

by _____

Dear Family: Please read the book with your child. Questions and prompts are labeled "Adult Says."

▲ End

Adult Says: At the end of the story, what hatched from the small egg?

Student Says: a duck

3

● Beginning

1

Student Says: It was small.

Adult Says: Four of the eggs were large. What about the fifth one?

Student Says: five eggs

Adult Says: At the beginning of the story, what did Mother Goose have?

■ Middle

Adult Says: In the middle of the story, what did the four baby geese hear?

Student Says: a strange noise

2

✄

I Fed

by _____

Dear Family: Have your child read the book with you.

a said, I fed the

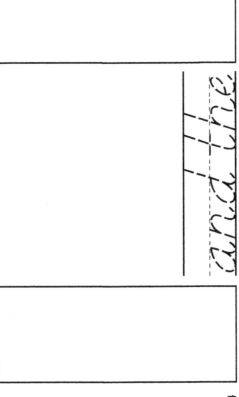

and the

4

31

a said, "I fed the

PREP: Copy one puzzle piece page per student on white paper. (You may wish to cut the puzzle pieces into three strips. Students can cut the strips into pieces or simply match and glue the strips to the frame.) Copy one frame per student on colored paper. Make a sample. Have extra copies of the puzzle pieces in case some get lost.

STUDENT DIRECTIONS: Color the puzzle pieces, if time allows. Cut out the puzzle pieces. Match and glue the pieces to the frame. Say the rhyming words.

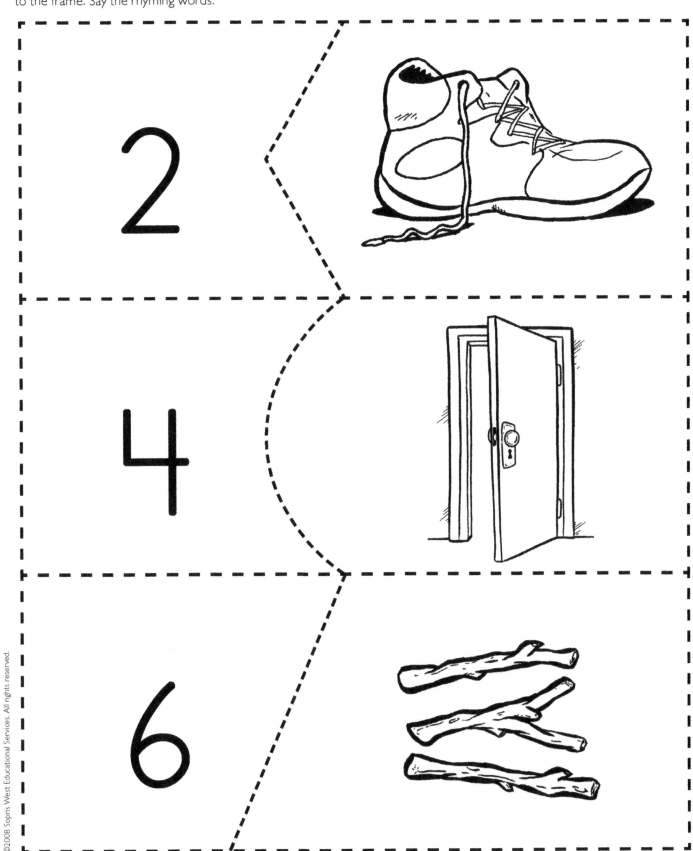

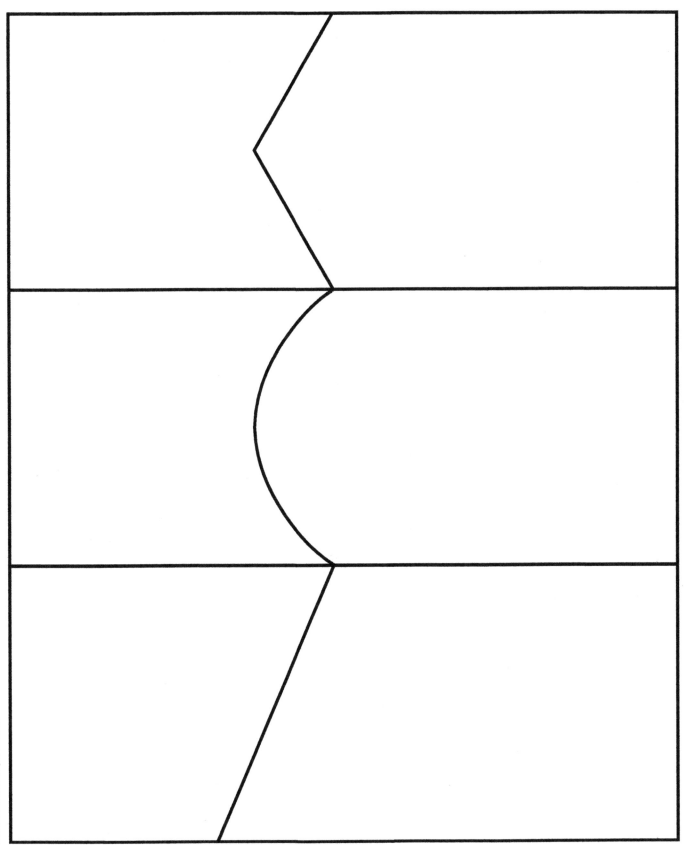

Dear Family: Have your child tell you the rhyming words.   I'm _____

I'm _____

Review

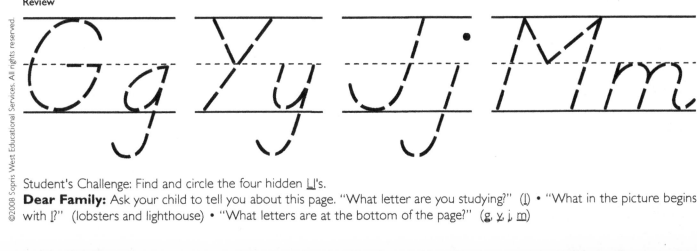

Student's Challenge: Find and circle the four hidden Ll's.

Dear Family: Ask your child to tell you about this page. "What letter are you studying?" (l) • "What in the picture begins with l?" (lobsters and lighthouse) • "What letters are at the bottom of the page?" (g, y, j, m)

I'm _____

My Letter L Book

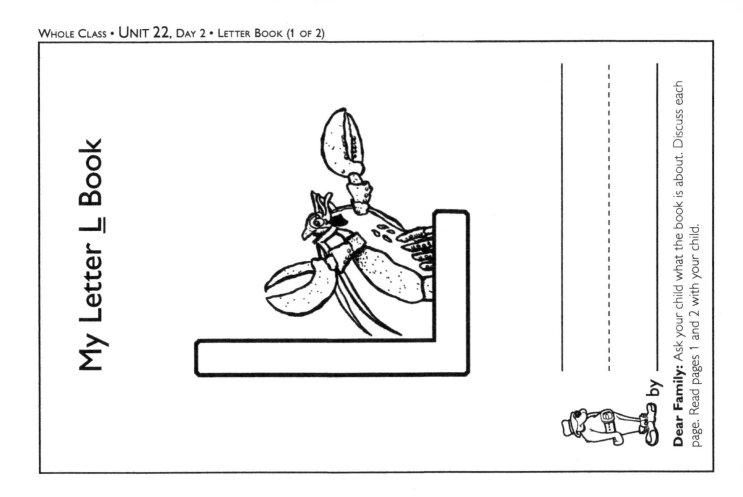

by _____

Dear Family: Ask your child what the book is about. Discuss each page. Read pages 1 and 2 with your child.

Other sounds I know about:

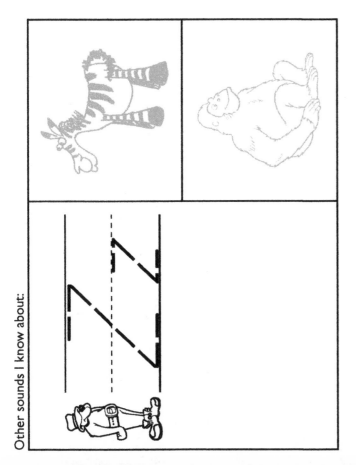

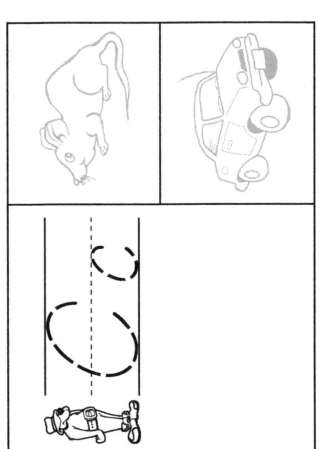

3 Have students cross out the picture that does not start with the sound.

See the

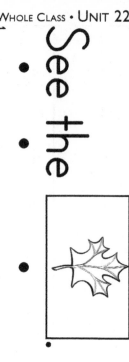

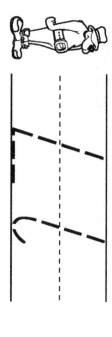

I see the

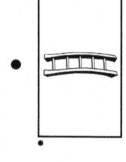

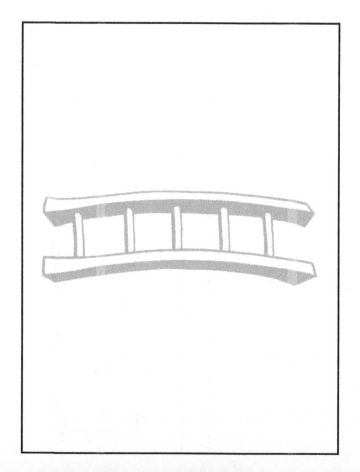

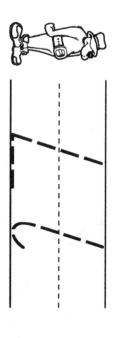

The Lobster Café
Retell Book

by _____

Dear Family: Please read the book with your child. Questions and prompts are labeled "Adult Says."

▲ End

Adult Says: At the end of the story, what did Lou get from his friends?

Student Says: a heart of gold

3

● Beginning

1

Adult Says: At the beginning of the story, what did it mean when Lobster Lou's antennae twitched?

Student Says: He was thinking about helping someone.

Adult Says: What did he do for Edith Eel?

Student Says: He gave her a job.

■ Middle

Adult Says: In the middle of the story, what did Edith Eel and the other sea creatures plan?

Student Says: a surprise party for Lobster Lou

2

I'm

STUDENT DIRECTIONS: Color and cut out the pictures. Then sort and glue them. Glue the things with an /ăăă/ sound under the circle with the <u>a</u>. Glue the things with an /ĕĕĕ/ sound under the circle with the <u>e</u>.

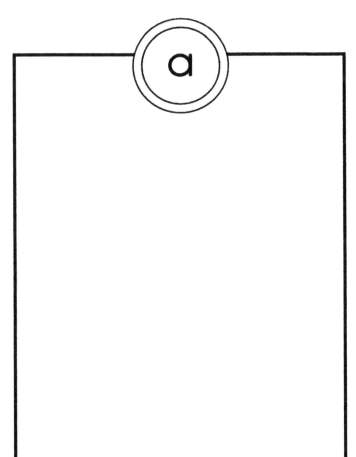

2

We See

_____

_____

by _____

Dear Family: Have your child read the book with you. (You will need to read the small text.)

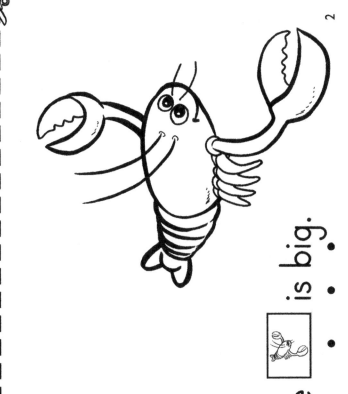

The [ ] is big.

What do you see in the sea?

7

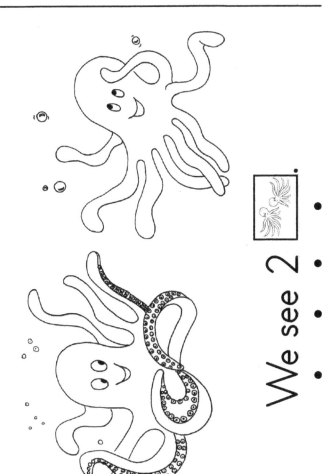

We see 2 [ ].

5

1

3

We see the

• .

We see 1

• .

We see the

• .

See the

• .

The is big.

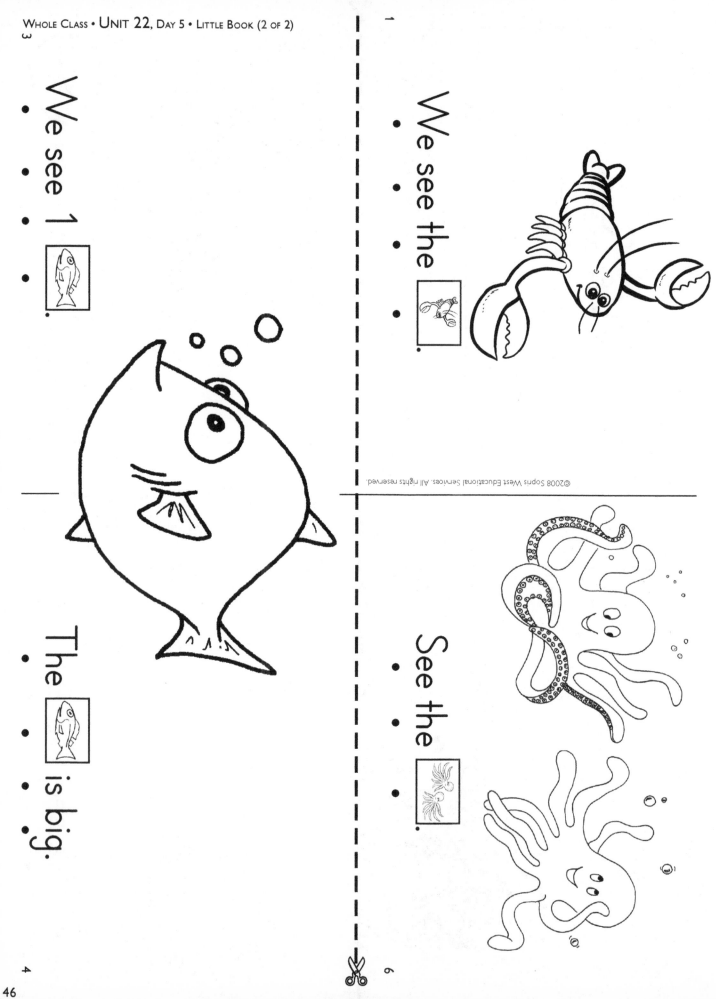

4

6

I'm _____

Review

Student's Challenge: Find and circle the four hidden Oo's.
Dear Family: Ask your child to tell you about this page. "What letter are you studying?" (o) • "What in the picture begins with o?" (octopus and office) • "What letters are at the bottom of the page?" (l, h, b, n)

I'm _____

My Letter O Book

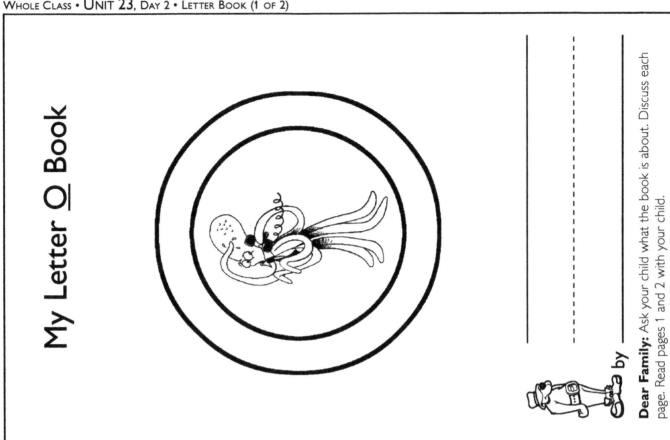

by _____

Dear Family: Ask your child what the book is about. Discuss each page. Read pages 1 and 2 with your child.

Other sounds I know about:

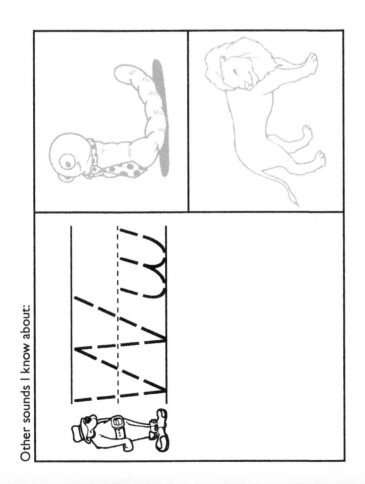

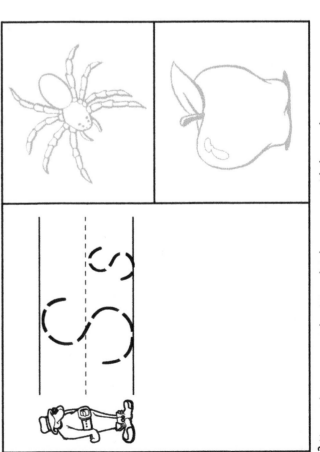

3 Have students cross out the picture that does not start with the sound.

I see the

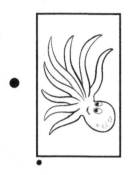

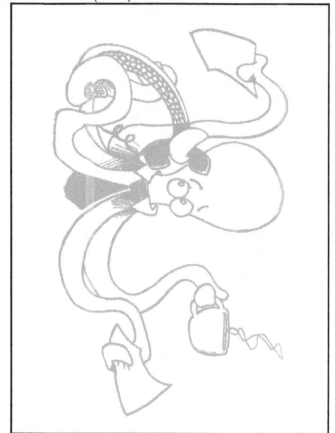

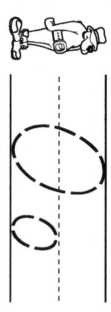

I see

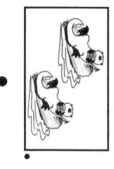

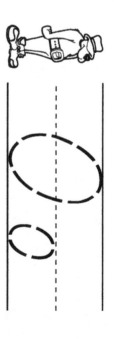

50

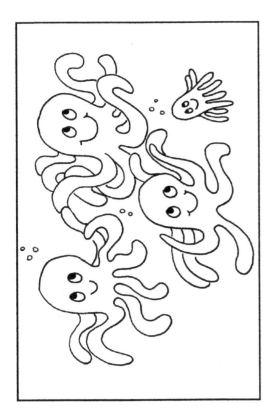

Octopus Facts

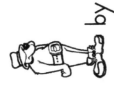

by _____

Dear Family: Please read the book with your child. Questions and prompts are labeled "Adult Says."

Adult Says: What's in the jar?

Student Says: an octopus

Adult Says: An octopus can squeeze into small spaces.

3

1

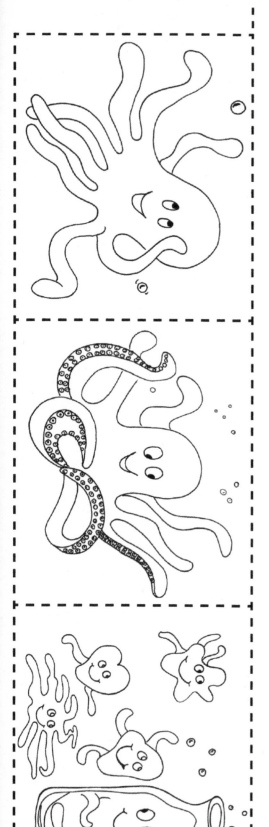

2

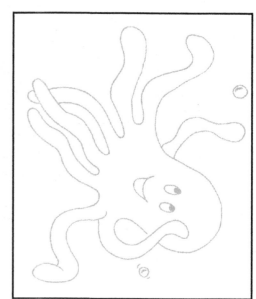

Adult Says: How many arms does an octopus have?

Student Says: eight

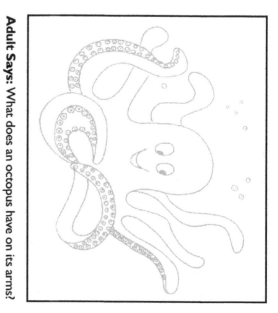

Adult Says: What does an octopus have on its arms?

Student Says: suckers

Adult Says: What does the octopus use its suckers for?

Student Says: catching food

I Have

by _____

Dear Family: Have your child read the book with you.

a said, I have

ten.

and ten.

4

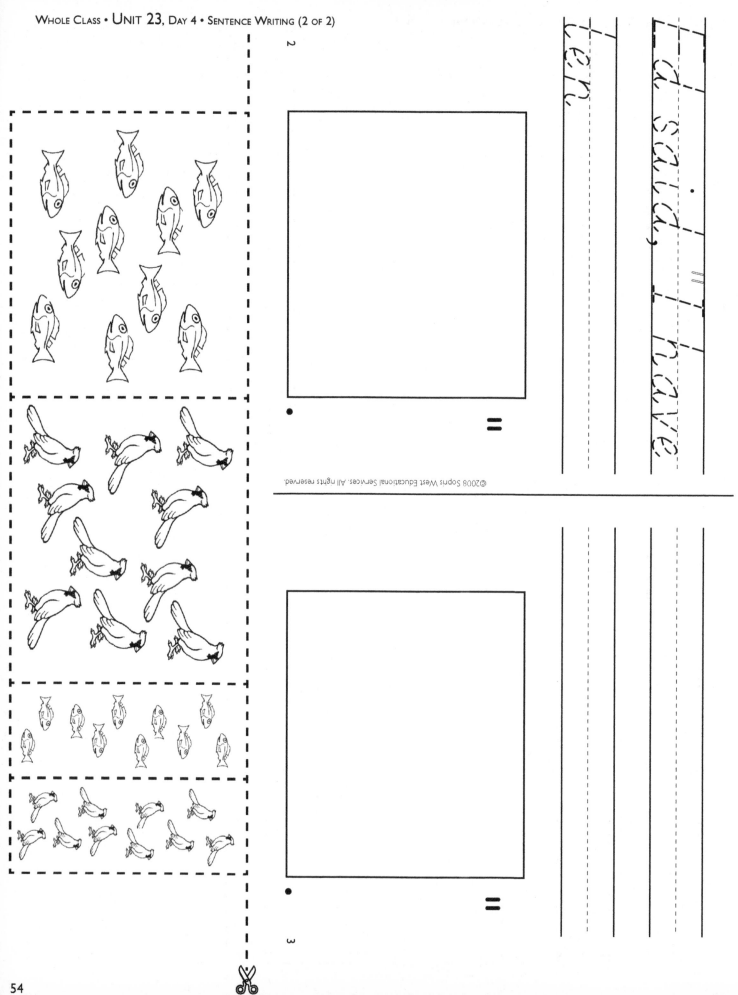

PREP: Copy one puzzle piece page per student on white paper. (You may wish to cut the puzzle pieces into four sections. Students can cut each section into two pieces or simply match and glue the sections as is to the frame.) Copy one frame per student on colored paper. Make a sample. Have extra copies of the puzzle pieces in case some get lost.

STUDENT DIRECTIONS: Color the puzzle pieces, if time allows. Cut out the puzzle pieces. Match and glue the pieces to the frame. Practice reading the words.

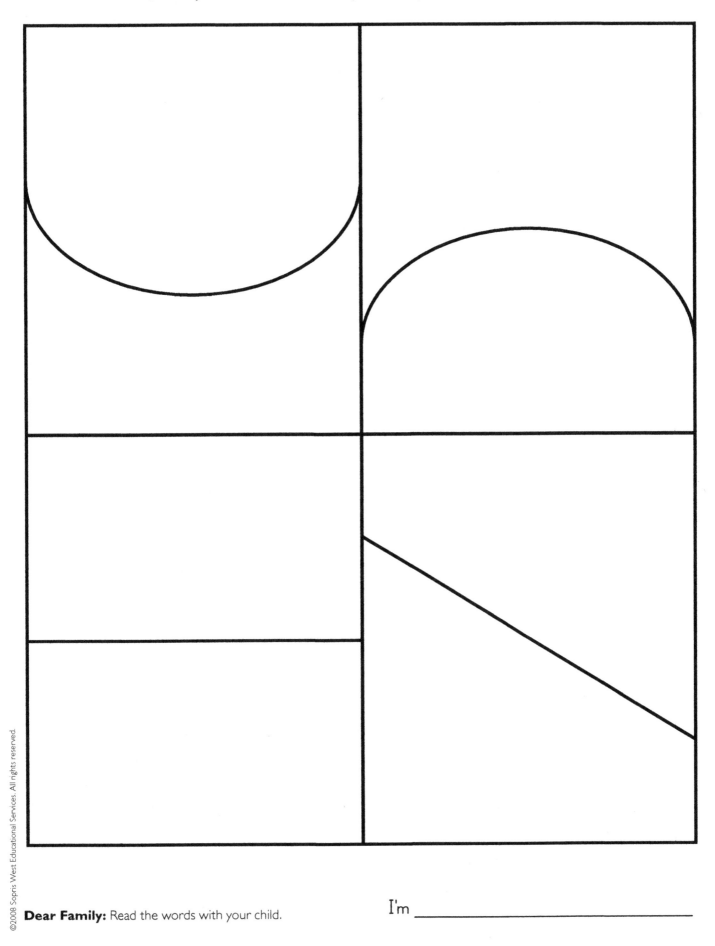

Dear Family: Read the words with your child.

I'm _____

I'm _____

Review

Student's Challenge: Find and circle the four hidden Qq's.

Dear Family: Ask your child to tell you about this page. "What letter are you studying?" (q) • "What in the picture begins with q?" (quails and quilt) • "What letters are at the bottom of the page?" (qu, o, f, p)

I'm _____

My Letter Q Book

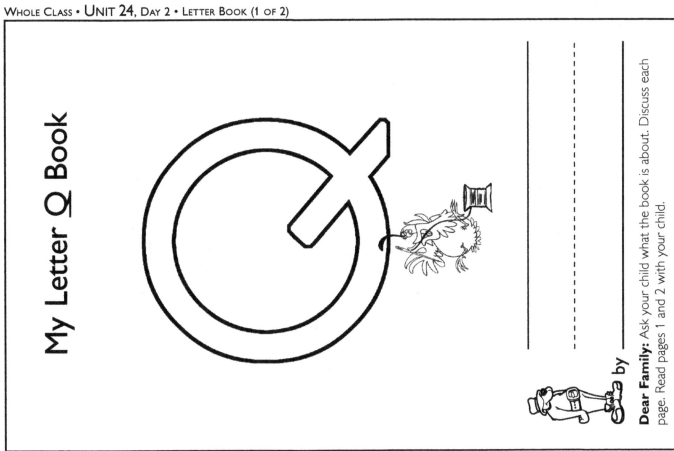

by _____

Dear Family: Ask your child what the book is about. Discuss each page. Read pages 1 and 2 with your child.

Other sounds I know about:

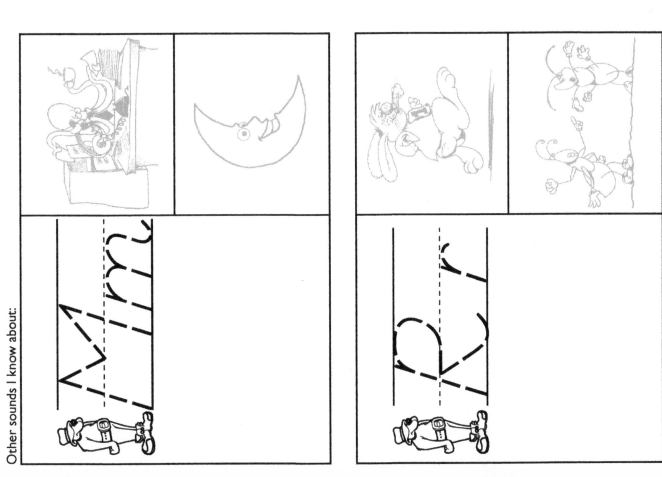

3 Have students cross out the picture that does not start with the sound.

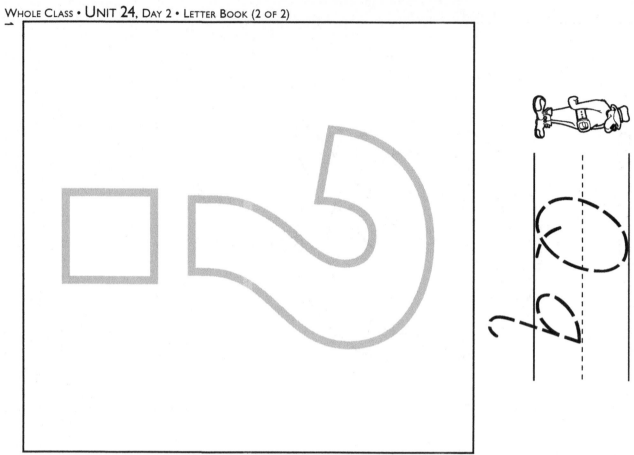

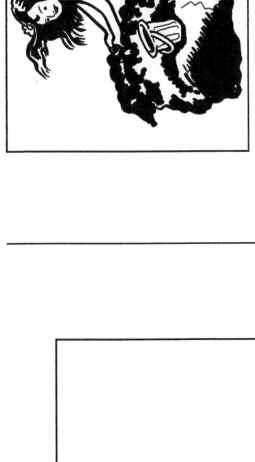

All About Malia

Retell Book

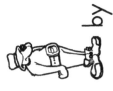

by _____

Dear Family: Please read the book with your child. Questions and prompts are labeled "Adult Says."

▲ End

Adult Says: At the end of the story, Malia's grandmother got well and made a quilt. Why does Malia look so happy?

Student Says: Malia's grandmother gave the quilt to Malia.

3

● Beginning

■ Middle

1

Adult Says: Who is the story about?

Student Says: Malia and her grandmother

Adult Says: Where did they live?

Student Says: in Hawaii

Adult Says: In the beginning of the story, what did Malia ask her grandmother to count?

Student Says: the grains of sand on the beach

Adult Says: What was the problem in the middle of the story?

Student Says: Malia's grandmother got sick.

2

I Have

by _____

Dear Family: Have your child read the book with you.

4

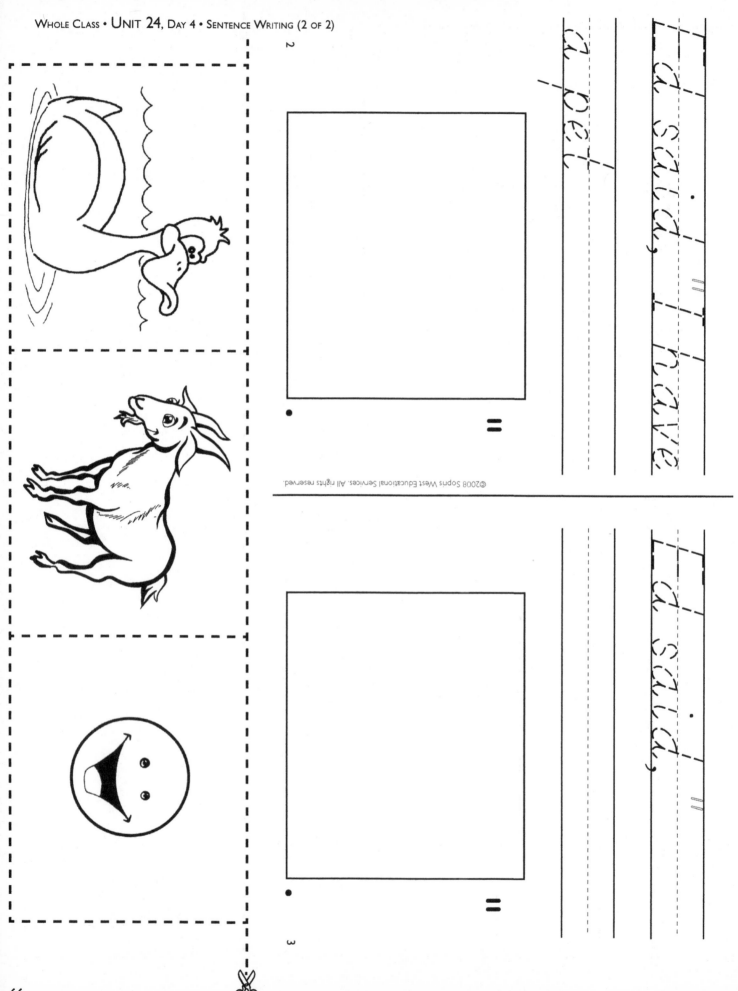

2

3

a said, I have a pet.

a said, a said,

2

Malia's Quilt

by _____

Dear Family: Have your child read the book with you.

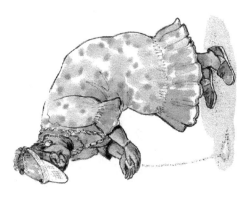

We see ___.

5

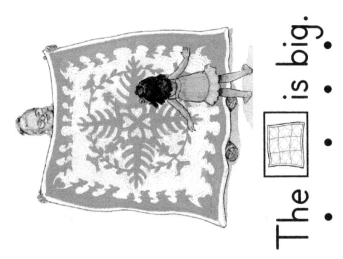

The ▦ is big.

7

I see ▦ and ▦.

5

3

1

We see

- •
- •

See the big

- •
- •
- •

We see the

- •
- •
- •

I see the 2

- •
- •
- •

6

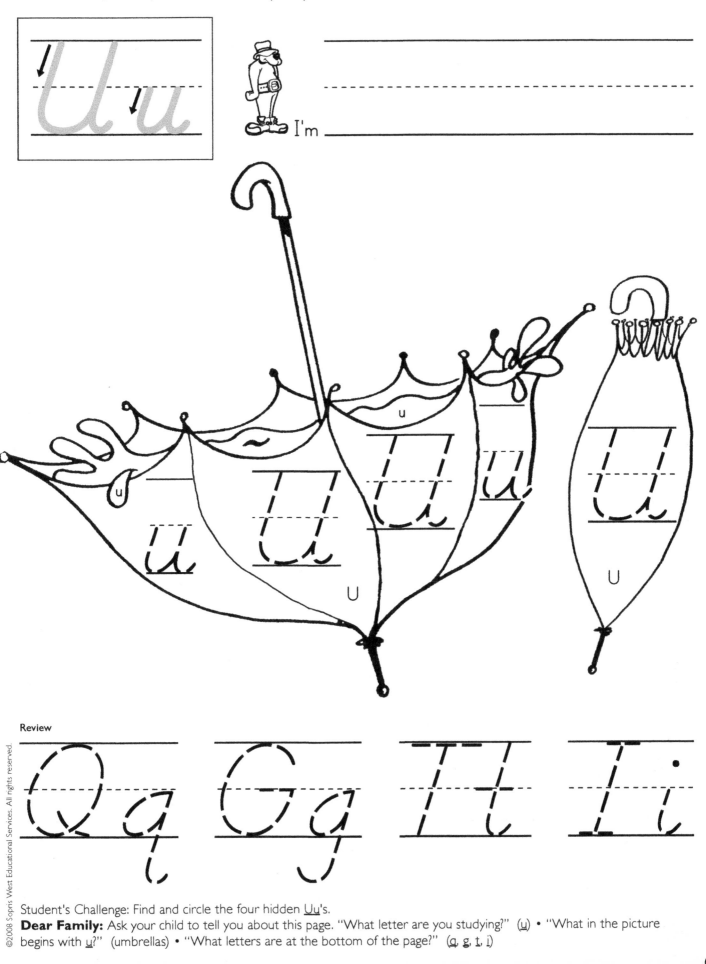

I'm

Review

Student's Challenge: Find and circle the four hidden Uu's.
Dear Family: Ask your child to tell you about this page. "What letter are you studying?" (u) • "What in the picture begins with u?" (umbrellas) • "What letters are at the bottom of the page?" (q, g, t, i)

69

I'm _____

My Letter <u>U</u> Book

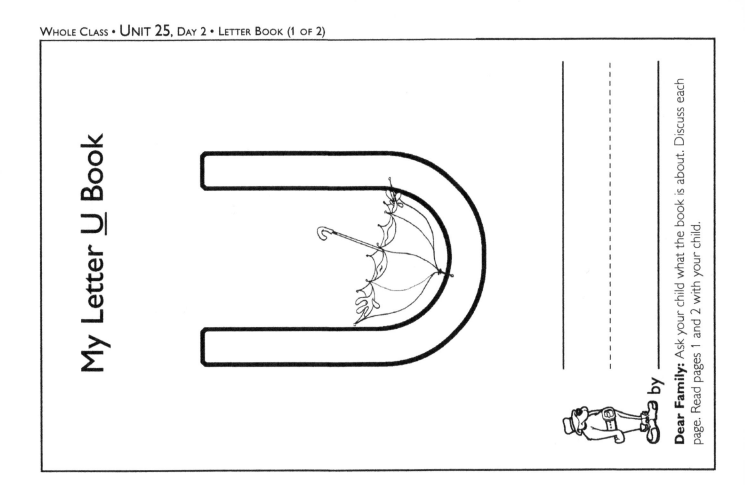

by _____

Dear Family: Ask your child what the book is about. Discuss each page. Read pages 1 and 2 with your child.

Other sounds I know about:

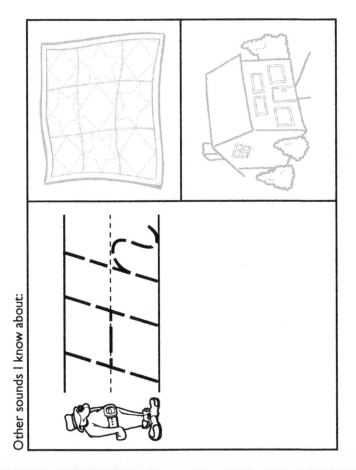

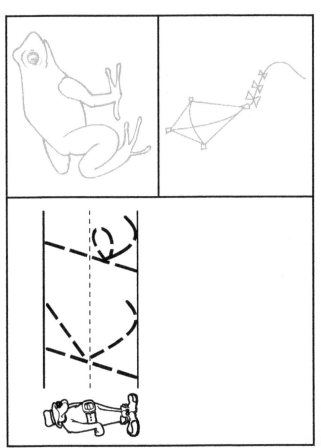

3 Have students cross out the picture that does not start with the sound.

I see the

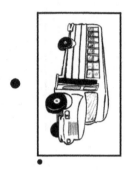

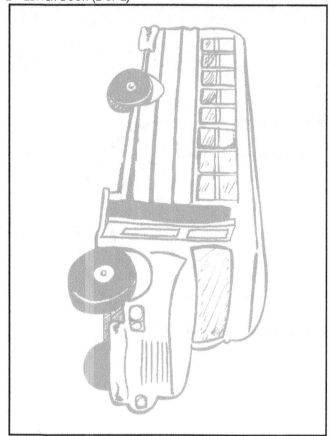

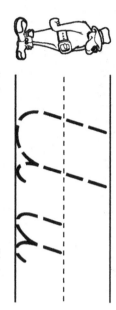

I see 2

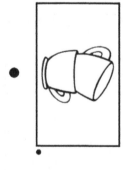

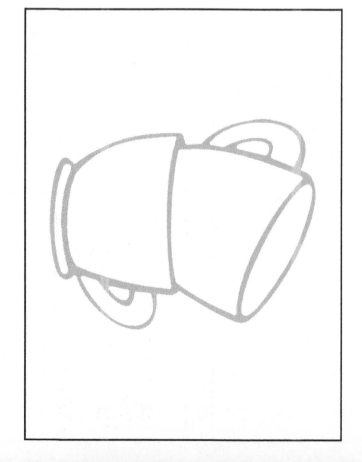

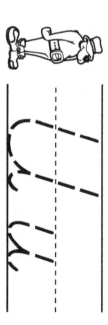

My Family

Photo Album

by

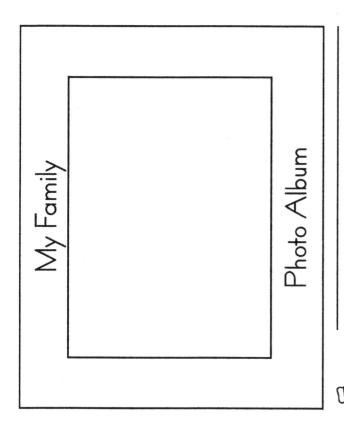

Dear Family: Please read the book with your child. Prompts are labeled "Adult Says."

Adult Says: Tell me about your picture.

3

1

My Home

My Favorite Place to Go

My Birthday

Adult Says: Tell me about your picture.

Adult Says: Tell me about your picture.

2

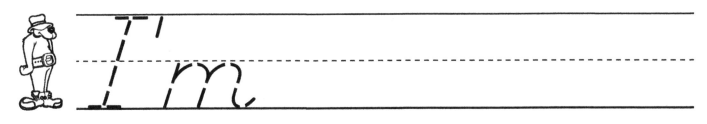

STUDENT DIRECTIONS: Color and cut out the pictures. Then sort and glue them. Glue the things with an /ŏŏŏ/ sound under the circle with the <u>o</u>. Glue the things with an /ĕĕĕ/ sound under the circle with the <u>e</u>.

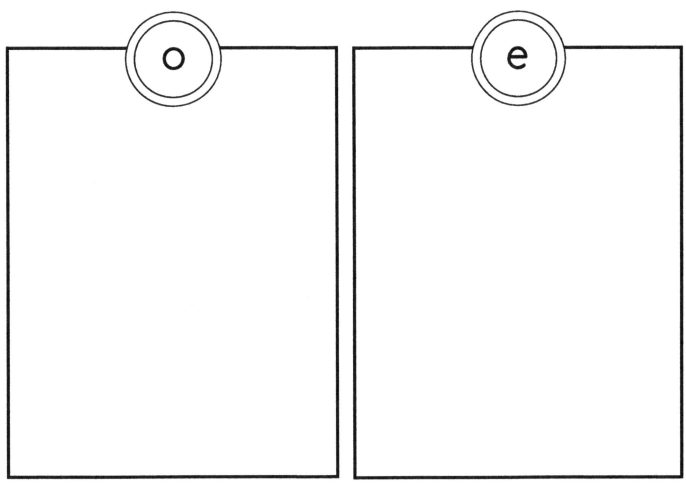

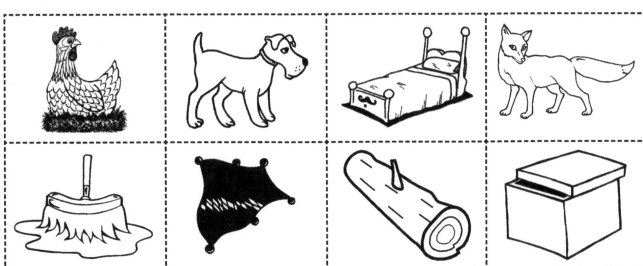

PREP: Copy one puzzle piece page per student on white paper. (You may wish to cut the puzzle pieces into four sections. Students can cut each section into two pieces or simply match and glue them as is to the frame.) Copy one frame per student on colored paper. Make a sample. Have extra copies of the puzzle pieces in case some get lost.

STUDENT DIRECTIONS: Color the puzzle pieces, if time allows. Cut out the puzzle pieces. Match and glue the pieces to the frame. Practice reading the words.

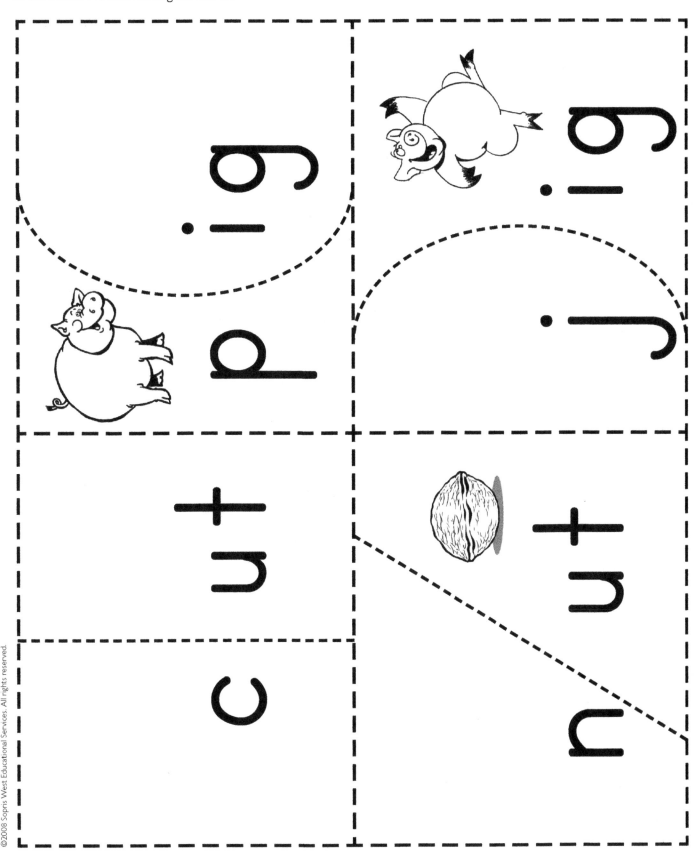

Dear Family: Read the words with your child.

I'm _____

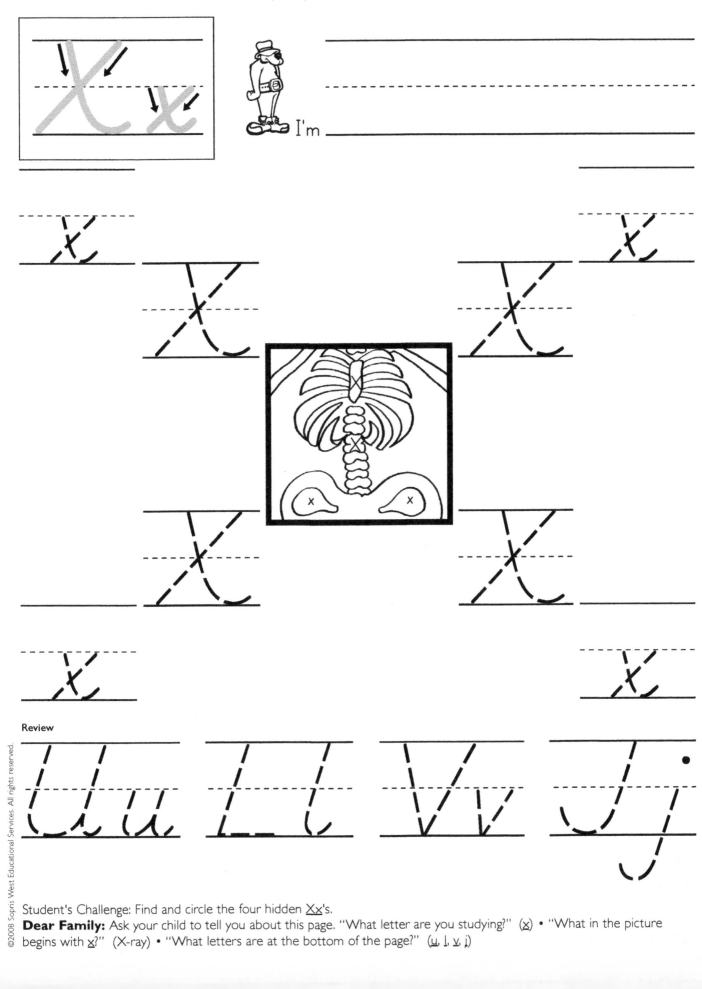

I'm

Review

Student's Challenge: Find and circle the four hidden Xx's.
Dear Family: Ask your child to tell you about this page. "What letter are you studying?" (x) • "What in the picture begins with x?" (X-ray) • "What letters are at the bottom of the page?" (u, l, v, j)

I'm _____

My ABC Book

_____

- - - - - - - - - - - - - - - - - -

by _____

Dear Family: Have your child share each page with you. Then read the ABC's with your child.

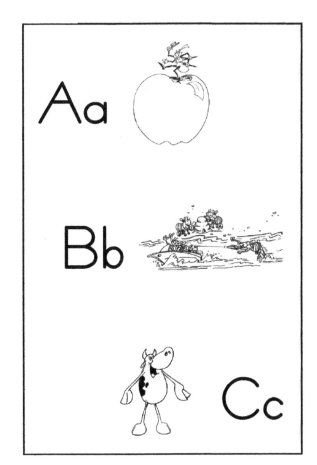

Aa

Bb

Cc

Dd

Ee

Ff

Gg

Hh

Ii

J j

K k

L l

M m

N n

O o

P p

Q q

R r

S s

T t

U u

V v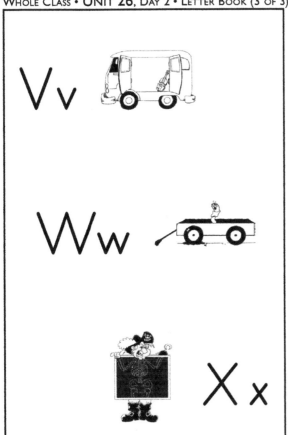

W w

X x

Y y

Z z

ABC's

Now I've sung my ABC's

A B C D E F
G H I J K L
M N O P Q R
S T U V W X
Y Z

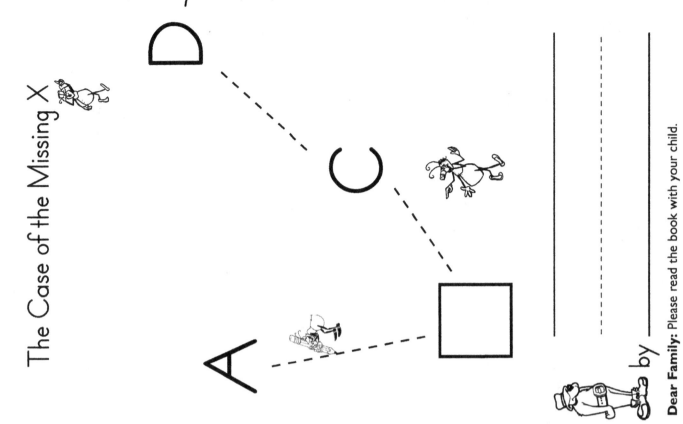

The Case of the Missing X

Dear Family: Please read the book with your child.

by _____

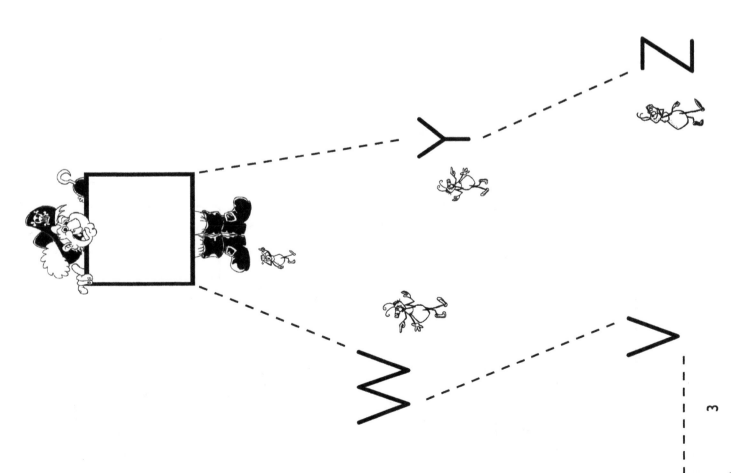

3

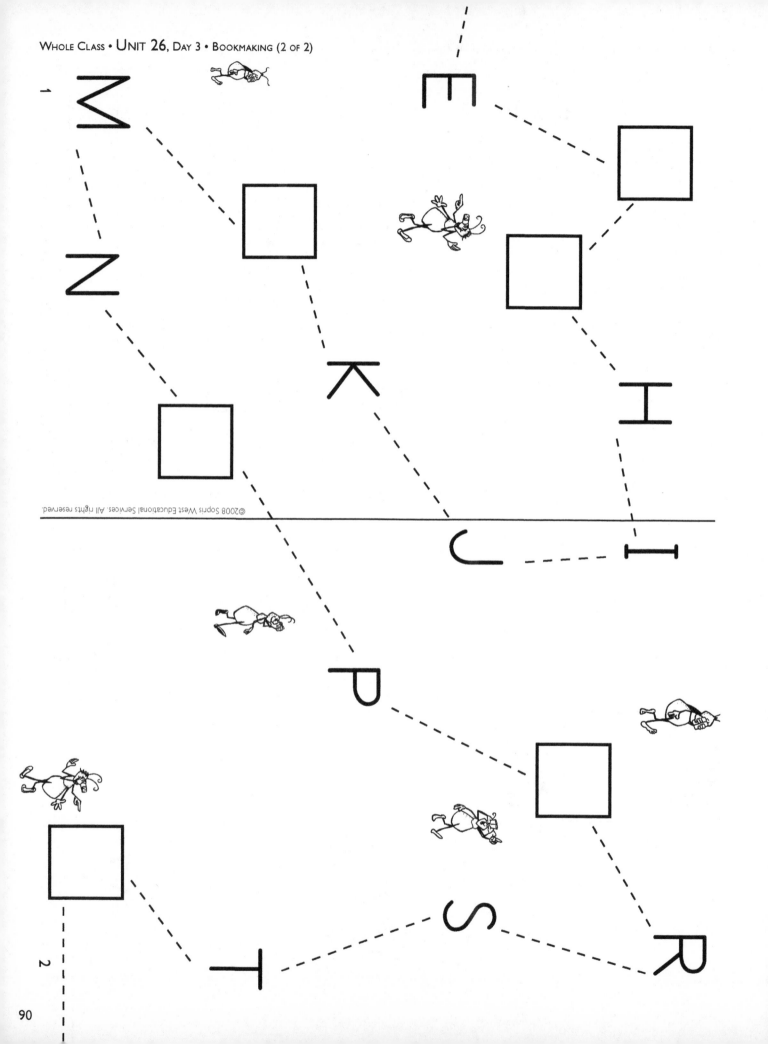

Ed Said

by _____

Dear Family: Have your child read the book with you.

4

dog

cat

pig

This is a ___.

a said,

This is a ___.

a said,

2

5

The ABC Mystery

by _____

Dear Family: Have your child read the book with you.

We see the 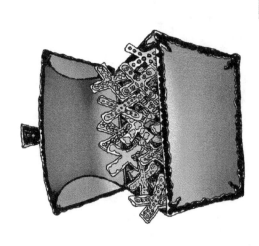.

We see the ▢.

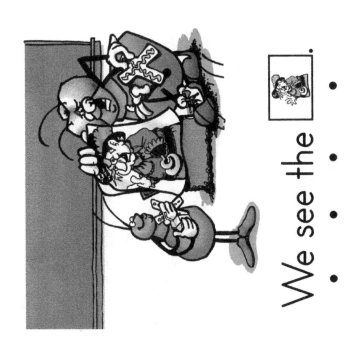

We see the ▢.

We see X's in the ▢.

7

5

3

1

See the sad .

The is in the .

See the .

I can see the X.

6

4

94

I'm _____

Review

Student's Challenge: Find and circle the four hidden <u>Ee</u>'s.
Dear Family: Ask your child to tell you about this page. "What letter are you studying?" (<u>e</u>) • "What in the picture begins with <u>e</u>?" (<u>E</u>d and <u>e</u>ngine) • "What letters are at the bottom of the page?" (<u>x</u>, <u>u</u>, <u>l</u>, <u>d</u>)

I'm _____

My Short Vowel E Book

by _____

Dear Family: Ask your child what the book is about and discuss each page.

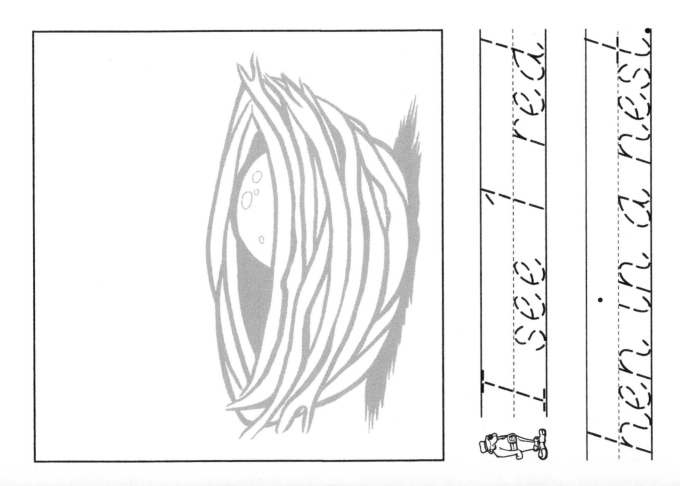

I see 1 red

hen in a nest.

men

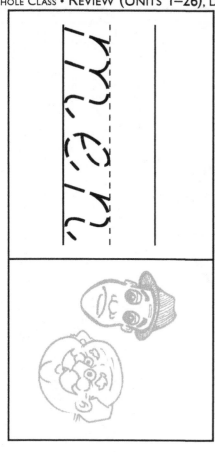

ten

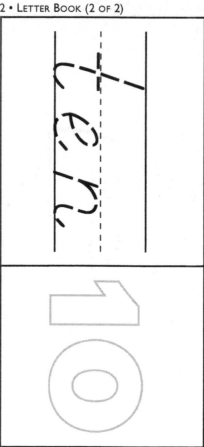

hen

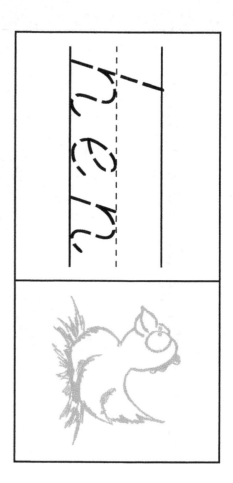

nest

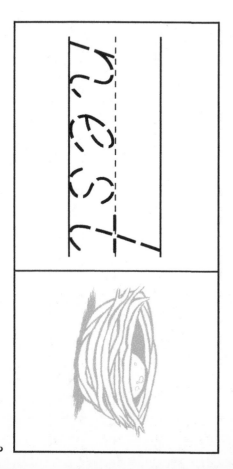

bed

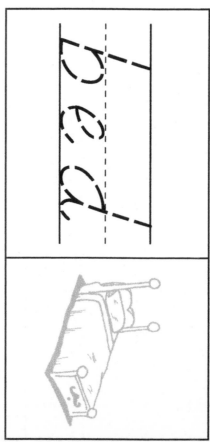

red

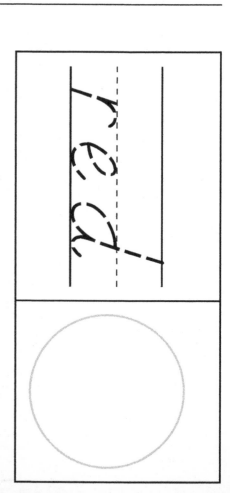

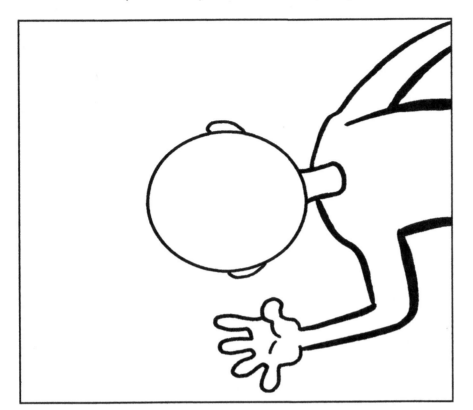

What I Learned This Year

_____

by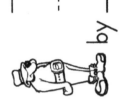

Dear Family: Please read the book with your child. Questions and prompts are labeled "Adult Says."

Adult Says: What did you learn this year?

I learned how to . . . .

_____

3

1

I learned how to . . .

Adult Says: What did you learn this year?

I learned how to . . .

Adult Says: What did you learn this year?

2

We Met

by _____

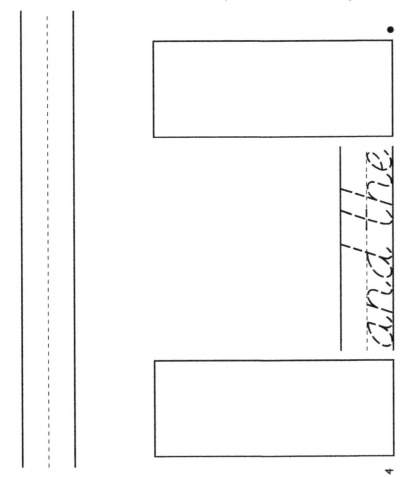

and the

4

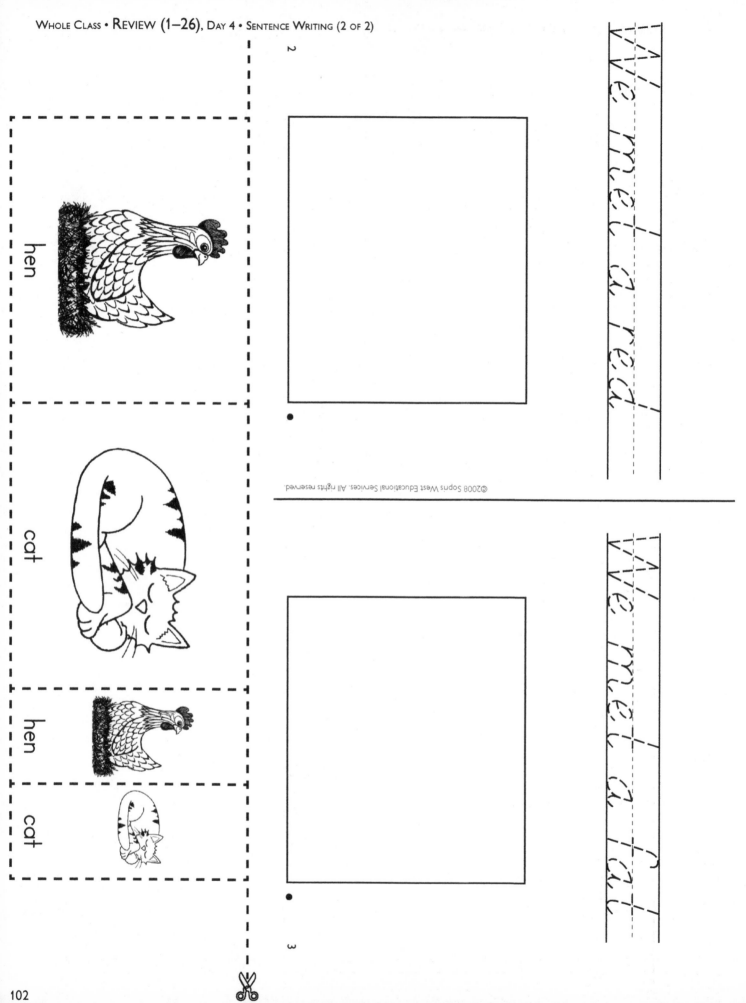

hen

cat

hen

cat

We met a red

We met a cat

2

3

2

In the Barn

by _____

Dear Family: Have your child read the book with you.

See the red hen.

See the pig and the hen in the

7

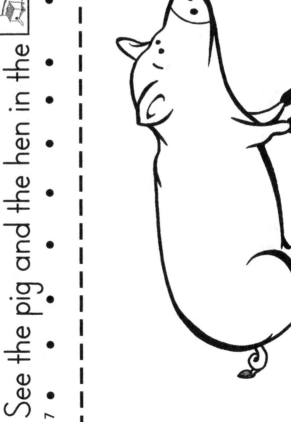

I see the big pig.

5

3

1

See 1 red hen in the .

See the 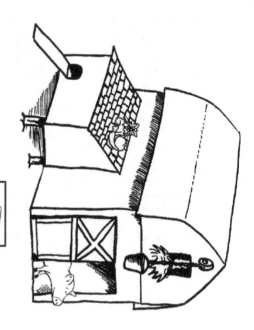.

I see the big pig in the 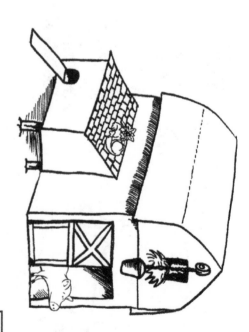.

See the pig.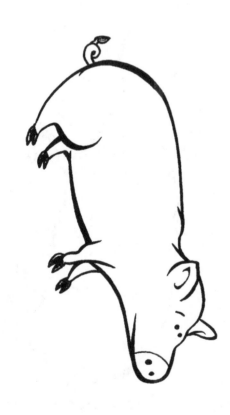

6

I'm _____

Dear Family: Ask your child to tell you about this page. For each letter, ask: "What letter do you see?" • "What sound does the letter make?"

I'm _____

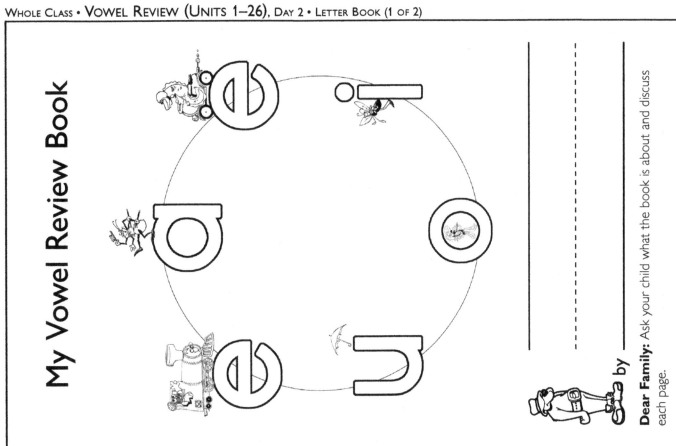

My Vowel Review Book

Dear Family: Ask your child what the book is about and discuss each page.

by _____

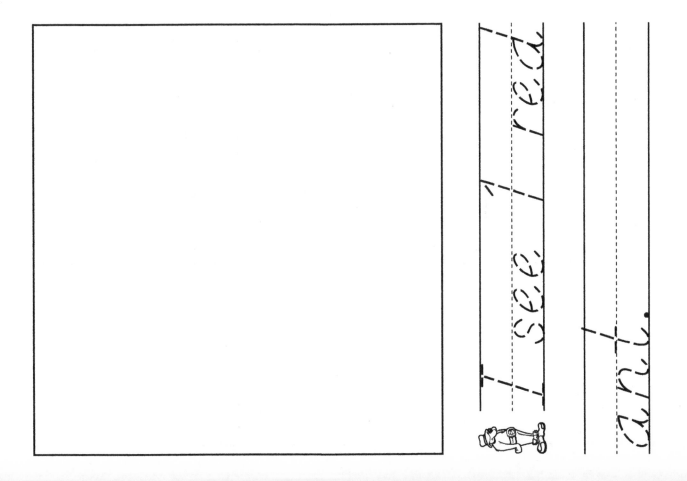

I see red

ant.

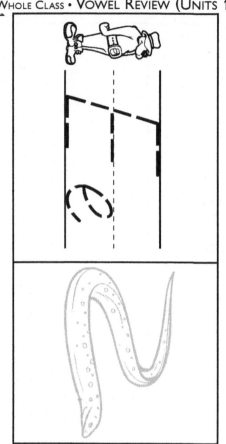

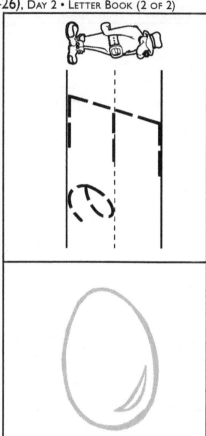

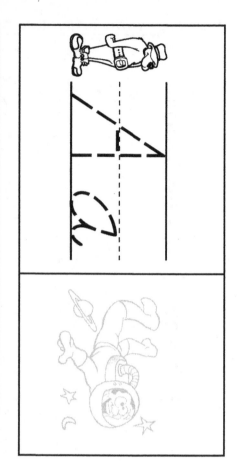

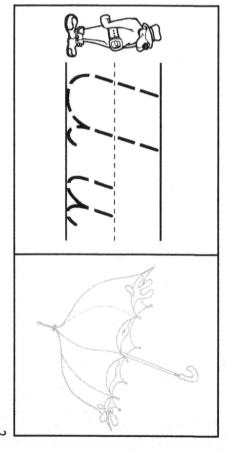

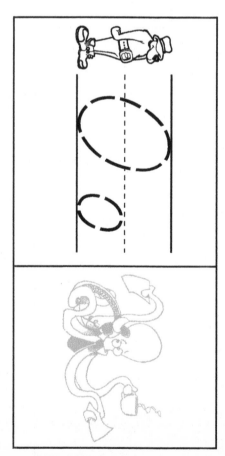

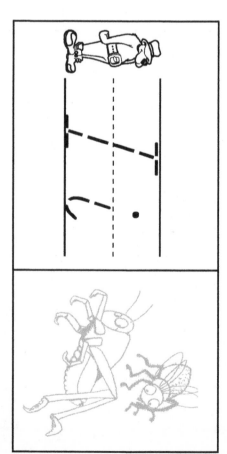

2

Where Is It?

_____
- - - - - - - -

by

Dear Family: Please read the book with your child.

The hen is in the nest.

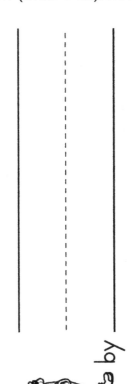

The dog is on the log.

7

The bee is in the ⬚.

5

1

- The bug is on the rug.

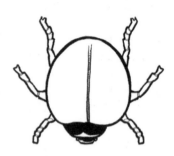

3

- The pig is in the pen.

6

- The cub is in the tub.

4

- The hat is on the cat.

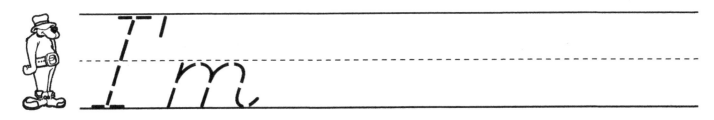

STUDENT DIRECTIONS: Color and cut out the pictures. Then sort and glue them. Glue the things with an /ŭŭŭ/ sound under the circle with the <u>u</u>. Glue the things with an /ĕĕĕ/ sound under the circle with the <u>e</u>.

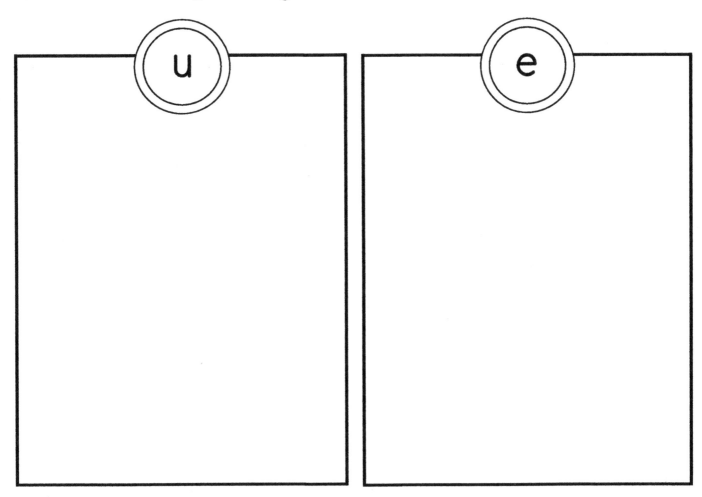

PREP: Copy one of each word page per student on white paper. (You may wish to cut the sentences into strips for your students to cut.) Copy one frame per student on colored paper. Make a sample. Have extra copies of the puzzle pieces in case some get lost.

STUDENT DIRECTIONS: Cut out the word boxes. Make sentences on your frame with the words. They can be long sentences or short sentences. Read the sentences to yourself or to a partner. Mix up your cards and make more sentences. Have fun!

am	I	see	See
We	can	the	The
is	sad	mad	
run	big	red	1

113

man

hen

Dear Family: Help your child make sentences with the word cards. Read the sentences and then mix the cards up and make new sentences. Have fun!

I'm _____